M INVENTS™

Much love!

D1548536

VOLUME ONE BY
REPLACE

Design & illustrations by Replace, Inc.

Published by Replace, Inc.
Minneapolis, Minnesota, USA
www.designreplace.com

Printed by PrintNinja
www.printninja.com
Printed in China

ISBN: 978-0-692-59725-5

PLEASE NOTE: *MN INVENTS* is a book of celebratory posters lovingly curated and
illustrated by designers living and working in Minnesota. It is not an encyclopedic
reference book compiled by academics or experts. Our research relied on readily
available sources such as Wikipedia. For more complete information, interested parties
should pursue their own research—which will only result in discovering stories that are
even deeper and richer than those presented here. Read on and enjoy!

A QUICK WORD FROM ROBERT STEPHENS, FOUNDER OF THE GEEK SQUAD

Minnesota was the best place for me to start The Geek Squad. Why did so many leading companies and brands emerge from Minnesota? What's so special about the place? Why, for example, do world leaders travel all the way to Rochester, Minnesota, for the best medical care in the world? Why is Minnesota such a great place to do business, and how did so many creative people end up here?

Because Minnesota is the Russia of America.

That's meant as a compliment. After all, some of the best poets and physicists come from Russia. Why? Because it is cold there; there's nothing to do but sit by the fire, read books, and strategize against your competition. I think that goes a long way to explain how Minnesota has birthed so many interesting companies and is such a great place to do business.

NERF
Reyn Guyer, Parker Brothers (1969)

Family-Friendly Firefights!

In 1969, St. Paul native Reyn Guyer, a 35-year-old inventor, approached game industry megastars Parker Brothers with a volleyball set he said was safe for indoor play. What a great idea—and an appropriate one for Minnesota winters, since volleyballs tend to ice up at -20 ºF! The pros at Parker Brothers studied Guyer's brainchild carefully and, proving that editing may be the most important element of invention, eliminated everything but its awesome foam ball. The Nerf revolution was born!

Nerf's original advertising read: "Throw it indoors; you can't damage lamps or break windows. You can't hurt babies or old people." And the simple idea behind it, of bringing outside fun inside, was tailor-made for the jumbo rec rooms of the era's burgeoning suburbs.

Since then, the quest to conquer the Great Indoors with more active play has spawned countless Nerf variations and other toys, from Nerf Sports to Nerf Blasters to Lazer Tag. Millions of hours of kiddie fun can be laid at the feet of this great Minnesota invention—one of the few rivals to screen time for kids with winter-induced cabin fever. And it still can't hurt babies or old people!

M INVENTS
NERF
INDOOR BALL

1969 **Reyn Guyer, Parker Brothers**
The famous Nerf ball was invented
by Minnesota-based inventor Reyn Guyer as an indoor
volleyball. It was originally marketed as a toy that
was safe for use near both babies and the elderly.
| mninvents.com | designreplace.com |

M INVENTS™

THE AMAZING

MIND CONTROLLED

FOUR-PROPELLERED

HELICOPTER

2013 University of Minnesota

A research team at the University of Minnesota developed a brain-to-computer interface that allows someone to fly a remote-controlled helicopter simply by thinking.

| mninvents.com | designreplace.com |

MIND-CONTROLLED HELICOPTER
University of Minnesota (2013)

Look Ma—No Hands!

Is it possible to control a helicopter with your mind? Thanks to Professor Bin He and a team of his students at the University of Minnesota, the answer is yes. It may seem like science fiction, but in 2013, the professor and his crew harnessed the power of thought to pilot a small quadcopter, using a noninvasive brain-to-computer interface.

It works like this: When the "pilot" imagines a movement, specific neurons in his brain produce electric currents. A special cap he is wearing detects those currents and translates them into impulses beamed to the copter via Wi-Fi. "Take off . . . Turn left . . . Turn right . . . Land"—all without lifting a finger!

But as fun as that may be, the goal of the technology is not to fill the sky with cool robotic aircraft. It was developed to help people with various disabilities and degenerative diseases enhance their mobility, independence, and communication, without requiring any implanted electronics. It just goes to show how bright ideas can bring sky-high expectations within reach!

DSV ALVIN
General Mills, Minneapolis (1964)

Go Deep!

The world's first deep-ocean submersible emerged from the most unlikely possible place: the Minnesota prairie. A division of Minneapolis innovator General Mills invented the 17-ton *DSV Alvin*, named after scientist and oceanographer Allyn Vine, on a commission from the United States Navy. The vessel made its first manned dive in 1965.

Alvin was designed to work at terrifying depths, in complete darkness. In the course of its 4,000-plus missions it has explored deep-sea thermal vents, searched for a hydrogen bomb lost in an Air Force accident, and visited the wreck of the *Titanic*. And, having undergone a number of overhauls and upgrades, it remains in service today, still going strong after a half-century of expeditions to our planet's deepest frontier.

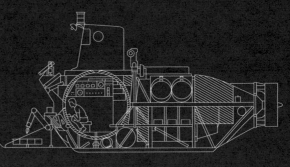

M
INVENTS ™

1964

General Mills, Minneapolis, MN

Owned by the US Navy and still in active service after almost 50 years, the manned, deep-ocean submarine Alvin has made over 4,000 deep-sea dives, including the exploration of the Titanic wreckage.

| **mninvents.com** | **designreplace.com** |

1ST DEEP-SEA SUBMARINE

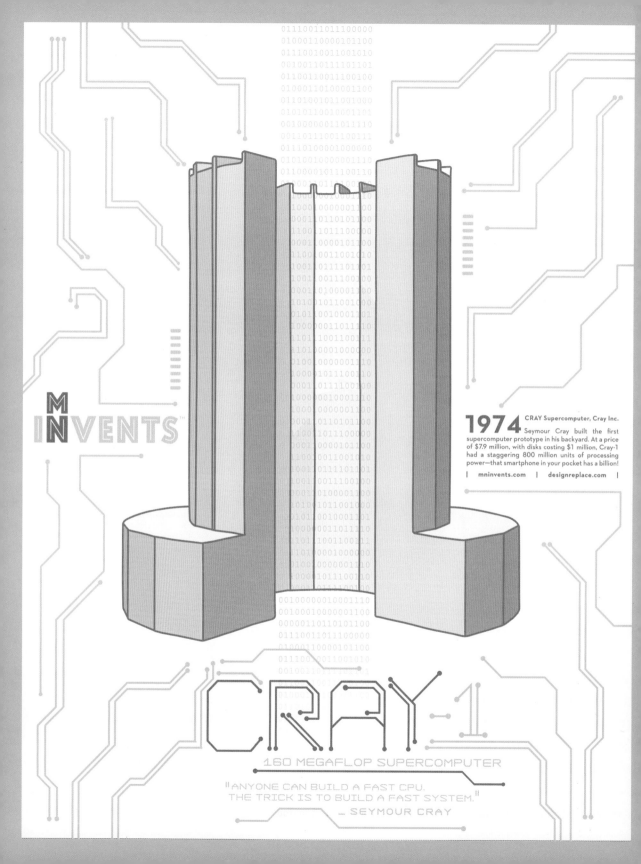

MN INVENTS™

1974 CRAY Supercomputer, Cray Inc.
Seymour Cray built the first supercomputer prototype in his backyard. At a price of $7.9 million, with disks costing $1 million, Cray-1 had a staggering 800 million units of processing power—that smartphone in your pocket has a billion!

| mninvents.com | designreplace.com |

CRAY-1

160 MEGAFLOP SUPERCOMPUTER

"ANYONE CAN BUILD A FAST CPU.
THE TRICK IS TO BUILD A FAST SYSTEM."
— SEYMOUR CRAY

CRAY-1
Seymour Cray, Cray Research, Inc. (1974)

Suddenly Seymour!

Do you love your smartphone? Your Xbox? Your Mac? Could you live without any of them? If not, you owe more than you may realize to the Byte Baron of Bloomington, Minnesota, Mr. Seymour Cray.

Honored now as "The Father of Supercomputing," Cray was working for Minnesota's innovative Control Data Corporation in the early 1960s when he developed the CDC 6600, generally considered the first successful supercomputer. An owlish monolith of wires, plastic, and metal, it looked like an escapee from the set of the movie *Forbidden Planet* and was three times faster than its nearest competitor. The first CDC 6600 was delivered in 1965 to Switzerland's CERN laboratory, the tech research brain-farm where the World Wide Web would be invented 24 years later.

The early 1970s saw the founding of Seymour's own company, Cray Research, Inc. Just a few years later, the firm would unveil the iconic Cray-1 supercomputer. Installed at Los Alamos National Laboratory in 1976, this megalith of memory became one of the best-known and most successful supercomputers in history.

Seymour Cray's colossally complex wonders of wiring and dazzling computational speed number among the proudest products of what would become Minnesota's "Silicon Prairie." Without their pioneering technology, the personal computing revolution could not have happened—and that smartphone of yours, and that Xbox, might never have left the realm of science fiction.

SPAM
Hormel, Austin, MN (1937)

Spam! Spam! Spam! Spam! Spam! Spam! Spam! Spam! Spam!

Austin, Minnesota—aka Spam Town, USA—is, proudly and beyond a shadow of a doubt, the canned-ham capital of the universe. Its trademark product, that vaguely gelatinous combination of starch, pork shoulder, and ham, was introduced in 1937 and rose to prominence during World War II. All across America, the Minnesota-made meat slid its way out of its familiar tin and onto the dinner plates of soldiers and wartime families suffering from meat shortages.

Debate still rages over the origin of the name, with claims made for abbreviations of "spiced ham," "shoulders of pork and ham," "special army meat," and "specially processed American meat," among other sources.

The war's end saw Spam transformed into an international commodity. Introduced to Asia by soldiers deployed to the Pacific, it became a staple in Hawaii, Japan, Korea, and many other countries, where it can be found fried, stewed, even substituting for fish on sushi. Unfortunately, its reputation among Americans as an unexciting, low-budget food also led to an association with that endless, dreary river of junk email that we call, well . . .

MINVENTS™

1937 Hormel, Austin, MN

The famous spiced luncheon meat in a can was created by Jay C. Hormel, son of Austin-based Hormel founder George C. Hormel, as a way to make use of underutilized pork shoulder.

| mninvents.com | designreplace.com |

C-1 AUTOPILOT

1942 Honeywell, Minneapolis
Founded as a heating company, Minneapolis-based Honeywell became a defense contractor during World War II. The C-1 Autopilot was first installed in the B-29 bomber and was later produced for civilian aircraft. Subsequent versions played an important role in the space program.

| mninvents.com | designreplace.com |

MINVENTS

C-1 AUTOPILOT
Honeywell, Minneapolis, MN (1942)

From the Furnace to the Front Lines!

Swiss-born inventor Albert Butz may seem like an unlikely candidate for the title "Pioneer of Aerospace Innovation." Certainly, the name of the firm he and his business partner founded in the 1880s, the Butz and Mendenhall Hand Grenade Fire Extinguishing Company, doesn't hint at anything so lofty. But when Butz's 1885 patenting of the "damper flapper" furnace thermostat aroused the interest of a company in Indiana, the power of the patent started the Honeywell Heating Specialty Company down the road to being a Fortune 100 firm that would be headquartered in Minnesota for nearly 100 years.

With World War II, Honeywell (the Minneapolis-Honeywell Regulator Company at that time) expanded its focus on thermostats to include aeronautics. Its work as a defense contractor saw the development of the electromechanical C-1 Autopilot, a crucial component of the air-war effort that was installed in American bomber planes with historic results.

Long after the war was over, the ever-diversifying Honeywell's innovations continued to find their way into the skies, even as far as outer space. Acquiring Sperry Aerospace, the company produced autopilot technologies that were instrumental in moon landings and space shuttle missions. And watching over it all, from his perch high in the branches of modern aviation's family tree? None other than Albert Butz.

RETRACTABLE SEATBELT
James Ryan, University of Minnesota (1963)

High-Impact Innovation at the Speed of Science!

James "Crash" Ryan was a pioneer at the (unfortunately literal) bleeding edge of collision engineering. A professor of mechanical engineering at the University of Minnesota, he earned his nickname by testing safety equipment using himself as a subject, driving into the walls of campus parking lots at unsafe speeds. For science!

Luckily, Ryan's quest to understand vehicular destruction in an up-close and personal way would lead to more than just a trail of crumpled cars. It also produced a number of life-saving innovations, including the retractable seatbelt and the indestructible airplane flight-data recorder, or "black box." His high-speed antics even brought him some celebrity status, when he dropped a car from a crane on TV's *Today Show*, dramatically illustrating the damage done by a deadly collision.

For years, Ryan took his show on the road, trying to convince Detroit automakers that seatbelts should be in every car in America. He lamented their fatal lack of interest in his invention: "It's such a silly thing, to allow people to become a statistic, by reason of death due to an automobile accident."

But his bold research finally paid off, when President Lyndon Johnson signed the Highway Safety Act in 1966. The new law mandated that all passenger vehicles be outfitted with safety belts by 1968. And with that, James "Crash" Ryan generated his biggest impact of all: A 2004 report estimated that safety belts had saved close to 180,000 lives between 1975 and 2003.

Better buckle up!

M INVENTS

RETRACTABLE SEATBELT

1963 James "Crash" Ryan, U of M
Although the seatbelt had been around before 1963, James "Crash" Ryan invented the one we use today. Ryan's belt was designed to lock in the event of an accident, making it much safer. The inventor's nickname came from his habit of using himself as a crash-test dummy in his tests.

| mninvents.com | designreplace.com |

THE FIRST
STORED MEMORY COMPUTER

1953 UNIVAC 1101, ERA

The very first commercial computer to use random access memory was created by Engineering Research Associates in St. Paul. Not exactly a desktop model: The UNIVAC 1101 was 38 feet long and 28 feet wide!

| mninvents.com | designreplace.com |

M INVENTS™

UNIVAC 1101
Engineering Research Associates (1953)

Cracking the Memory Mystery!

The complicated story behind the birth of the first stored-program computer involves the Cold War battle for technical supremacy, a mountain of lawsuits, hundreds of the smartest people on earth, and a lot of blood, sweat, and bytes. But at the heart of it is a team of Navy cryptologists working out of a former glider factory in St. Paul, MN.

Engineering Research Associates (ERA) was created, with Navy help, just after World War II. The idea behind it was to keep a crack team of wartime code crackers gathered under one roof, to guarantee the Navy's continued access to their collective talents. But the project's payoff would be much bigger: With the firm's introduction in 1951 of the ERA 1101, later renamed UNIVAC 1101, this hotbed of innovative people and Atomic Age concepts would help create the modern computer industry.

Prior to the 1101, a computer was programmed for one specific task. If the required task changed, the computer could not change along with it. The brainiacs at ERA realized that, to suit a wide range of uses, a computer needed to be able to operate on whatever changeable programming was loaded into it. Their answer? "Drum memory," whose original version consisted of magnetic tape glued to a steel drum. The computer would "read" the spinning drum and be told exactly what to do.

That changed everything. Now you could store and remove programs at will, and alter a computer's function by writing new software to suit whatever job needed doing. That opened up computing to an unlimited range of possible applications, turning the formerly specialized apparatus into a versatile consumer device.

THE BUNDT PAN
Nordic Ware, Minneapolis, MN (1950)

The Volcanic Cake of Sheer Awesomeness!

In 1950, Minnesota's Nordic Ware company shook up the home-baking universe with a New World adaptation of an Old World treat. Their new product produced a cake in the shape of the classic European *Bundkuchen* (or *Gugelhupf*). In order to obtain a trademark for it, however, they had to change the name a little. So they added the letter T. Hello, Bundt pan!

The Bundt pan was slow to catch on at first, and narrowly missed being discontinued. But when it was featured in 1963's best-selling *New Good Housekeeping Cookbook*, its success was assured. Its star rose even further in 1966, when Ella Helfrich took home $5,000 and a trophy for her "Tunnel of Fudge" Bundt cake entry in the annual Pillsbury Bake-Off.

To date, Nordic Ware has sold more than 60 million Bundt pans.

The Bundt Pan

M INVENTS™

1950 Nordic Ware, Minneapolis, MN
Charged with creating a pan that could bake a more dense, European-style cake, Nordic Ware founder H. David Dalquist invented the iconic bundt pan, a round baking pan with a hole in the center.

| mninvents.com | designreplace.com |

SCOTCH TAPE

SCOTCH TAPE
3M (1930)

A Joke that Stuck like Glue!

Despite the plaid on the package, there's nothing Scottish about Scotch tape. In fact, the name originated as a play on the popular notion of the Scots being just a little too thrifty. The story goes that when a sticky tape, devised in the 1920s by Richard Drew at Minnesota Mining and Manufacturing, wasn't quite sticky enough, the man testing it told him, "Take this tape back to those Scotch bosses of yours and tell them to put more adhesive on it!"

When Drew invented cellophane tape in 1930, the folks at 3M picked up on the original joke and ran with it, turning what started out as a slight into a globally recognized brand name. Eventually 3M would sell Scotchgard, Scotch-Brite, Scotchlite, and Scotch brand audiotape, among other familiar products, all of them adorned with the trademark tartan pattern. To help drive the point home, a catchy little character named Scotty McTape would, beginning in the 1950s, become a familiar presence in 3M's TV advertising.

THE HANDLED GROCERY BAG
Walter Deubener, St. Paul, MN (1912)

Yes, Even THAT *Had to Be Invented!*

In 1912, grocery store owner Walter Deubener became a pioneering figure in the fine art of produce peddling, thanks to his clever solution to a common problem. The problem was, customers were reluctant to purchase more goods than they could comfortably carry. That obviously limited how much Deubener could sell, so he set himself the task of changing that somehow.

The answer came to him in a dream one night, waking him up from his sleep. If his customers wouldn't buy more than they could handle, he figured, he knew just how to handle it: He'd make an easy-to-handle paper sack—with string handles!

In the process of engineering his product, Deubener found that lacing string handles through holes in the bags also reinforced their base, allowing them to accommodate even more weight. The result? Soaring profits for Deubener and his wife, Lydia—as full-time bag manufacturers.

The Deubeners left a legacy of business savvy that is honored annually with the awarding of the Walter and Lydia Deubener Small Business Awards, presented by the St. Paul Area Chamber of Commerce in recognition of business innovation. Topping off a lifetime of philanthropy, their lavish lake home was donated after their passing and is now the site of Courage North, a facility for hearing-impaired and disabled teens and adults.

THE HANDLED GROCERY BAG

M
INVENTS™

1912 **Walter Deubener, St. Paul**
Concerned about his customers' ability to safely carry heavy loads of groceries, St. Paul shop owner Walter Deubener came up with a structurally stable way to attach string handles to an ordinary shopping bag. His innovation changed the way we shop, and it saved floors and sidewalks everywhere from dozens and dozens of broken eggs.

| mninvents.com | designreplace.com |

INVENTS™ **1977** Dr. Spencer Silver & Art Fry, 3M | mninvents.com | designreplace.com |

3M launched these as "Press 'n Peel" in a trial run in 1977, but they didn't take off. But when customers who were given free samples responded enthusiastically, the name was changed: On April 6, 1980, the product was reintroduced in US stores as Post-its.

POST-IT NOTES
Spencer Silver & Art Fry, 3M (1977)

An Idea that Didn't Stick . . . Much . . .

The year was 1968, and amid the cultural upheaval raging across America, a researcher at 3M ("Minnesota Mining and Manufacturing," dontcha know) was quietly plotting a revolution in office doodling. What Dr. Spencer Silver actually had in mind was a super-strong chemical adhesive. But as luck and innovation often have it, what he came up with was just the opposite: a "low-tack," reusable, pressure-sensitive adhesive that seemed to be of little potential use to 3M.

For five long years, Silver lobbied for acceptance of his "Solution without a problem." But his efforts, both formal and informal, failed to gain a foothold for his brainchild. Then, in 1974, Art Fry, a colleague who had attended one of Silver's seminars, got the notion to use the glue to anchor a bookmark in his hymnbook. Taking advantage of 3M's officially sanctioned "permitted bootlegging" policy, Fry developed the idea into the yellow Post-it notes that we now use by the truckload. But even their familiar color came about by accident: The supply of scrap paper in the lab just happened to be yellow!

FIRST INDOOR SHOPPING MALL
Victor Gruen, Edina, MN (1956)

Perfect Weather for Shopping!

In 1956, in Edina, Minnesota, Southdale Center opened its doors to a new breed of American shopper. The fully enclosed, climate-controlled retail complex said goodbye to the mere window-shopper, who might be reluctant to doff her winter hat and mittens with every store she visited, only to have to suit up again when she left. For a car-owning, newly mobilized consumer middle class, the indoor shopping mall became an all-season mecca for families looking to spend an afternoon in perfect comfort, safe from the freezing-to-sweltering extremes of Minnesota's weather.

Austrian architect Victor Gruen conceived of the indoor mall as a social gathering place akin to the city squares of his native Vienna. His vision included art, fountains, tropical plants—even an aviary complete with wild birds. And while his Southdale Center lacks a few features of the original design, it still thrives today, having undergone several expansions in order to compete with the Mall of America, its gargantuan grandchild.

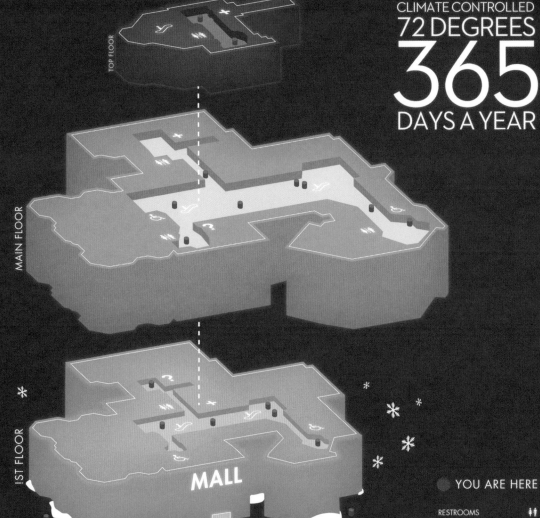

FIRST INDOOR SHOPPING MALL

CLIMATE CONTROLLED
72 DEGREES
365
DAYS A YEAR

TOP FLOOR

MAIN FLOOR

1ST FLOOR

MALL

YOU ARE HERE

RESTROOMS
GUEST SERVICES
FIRST AID
ESCALATORS
WHEELCHAIR ACCESS
STAIRS
ELEVATORS

M
INVENTS™

1956 **Southdale Mall, Edina, MN**
Southdale Center in Edina, MN,
is the oldest fully climate-controlled indoor shopping
center. The Austrian-born architect Victor Gruen
modeled it on the arcades of European cities.

| mninvents.com | designreplace.com |

Rollerblades

M INVENTS™

1979 Scott & Brennan Olson

In 1979, the Olson brothers decided they could improve on the inline skates available at their local sporting goods store. Working from their parents' basement, they purchased the patent and refined the design in a number of ways, and the Rollerblade was born.

| mninvents.com | designreplace.com |

ROLLERBLADES
Scott & Brennan Olson, Minneapolis, MN (1979)

Hockey . . . in the Summer!

At the age of 19, an aspiring Minnesota hockey goalie named Scott Olson started brainstorming on a way to improve his brother Brennan's inline skates. He was convinced of the potential of an upgraded version, and he got so swept up in the challenge that he eventually bought the patent.

Incorporating a series of tweaks and twists—softening the wheels, adding speedy bearings, and using a hockey boot instead of a skate shoe—Olson began marketing his better product to hockey players and coaches directly, with a money-back guarantee. The momentum grew, and the perfected skate, which he named the Rollerblade, became a sidewalk sensation.

A series of buyouts and deals led to Scott Olson leaving his own company, but not before it had made him rich. He continues to work from his farm in Waconia, Minnesota, where evidence of new inventions is everywhere to be seen.

TONKA TRUCK
Mound Metalcraft Company (1946)

Tiny Trucks! Heavy Duty!

In 1946, Mound Metalcraft started down the road to magic when it moved into a former toy factory. E. C. Streater, the toymaker's previous proprietor, approached Mound with a number of his patented toys and new designs. Soon the garden implement company's stamped-steel production facilities were cranking out miniature metal construction cranes.

The toy line proved popular enough to merit its own brand, and Tonka Toys Incorporated was born. The name was derived from a Dakota Sioux word meaning "big." And indeed, Tonka Trucks were suddenly a *tonka* success!

Decades later, the familiar yellow Tonka Trucks continue to be a mainstay of imaginary construction sites in backyard sandboxes around the globe, and in 2001 they were inducted into the National Toy Hall of Fame. Tonka now makes an array of molded plastic trucks to go with their stamped-steel classics.

TONKA TRUCK

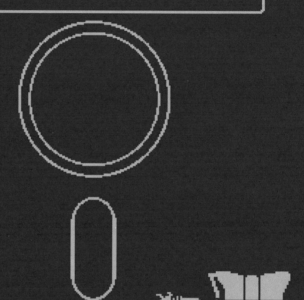

OREGON TRAIL

YOU HAVE DIED OF DYSENTERY.

M INVENTS™

1971 **Rawitsch, Heinemann & Dillenberger (MECC)**
The Oregon Trail was a computer game originally developed in 1971 and produced by the Minnesota Educational Computing Consortium (MECC) in 1974. The notoriously difficult game put players in the shoes of pioneers, setting various perils in their paths that corresponded to the hardships described in the journals of actual travelers on the Trail. | mninvents.com | designreplace.com |

OREGON TRAIL
Don Rawitsch, Bill Heinemann & Paul Dillenberger (1971)

You Have Dysentery, Sally Has Measles, Mary Died of Typhoid Fever, and Everybody's Got Cholera—Have a Nice Trip!

Who would have guessed that what young children needed in the early 1970s to advance their education and computer literacy would be a good case of dysentery? Destined to provide an impressive illustration of how to excite kids about history, the game *The Oregon Trail* was developed by Don Rawitsch, Bill Heinemann, and Paul Dillenberger in 1971 and produced by the Minnesota Educational Computing Consortium (MECC) in 1974.

The aim of this early computer game was simple: to teach schoolchildren about the realities of 19th-century pioneer life. But its effect would be revolutionary, as it set the kids' minds ablaze over this one small facet of America's past. How? By putting them into the role of trailblazer themselves. And as they lived it they came to love it, even though it subjected them—imaginatively speaking, that is—to all the deadly, horrible risks of traveling the frontier in a covered wagon. Go figure!

However you explain its success, *The Oregon Trail* fostered such passionate engagement that it would influence the next 45+ years of both game play and educational theory.

ORGAN TRANSPLANTS
University of Minnesota (1966)

A Home Team with a Lot of Heart . . . and Kidneys, and . . .

Over the last half-century, the University of Minnesota has been a leader in the surgical field, charging along at the, um, cutting edge of medical innovation. It was there, after all, that Doctors William Kelly and Richard Lillehei performed the world's first kidney-and-pancreas transplant, in 1966, following it that same year with the first intestinal transplant. And while Minnesota wouldn't see its first heart transplant until 1978, Christiaan Barnard, the doctor behind the world's very first one (in 1967), was trained at none other than the U of M.

In short, in the transplant game, you could say the University of Minnesota has compiled some very impressive career stats: It transplanted its 700th liver in 2003 and its 700th heart in 2010, and performed its 8,000th kidney transplant in 2013.

Now *that* is a winning team!

MN INVENTS™

1966 University of Minnesota

The very first successful pancreas transplant was done at the University of Minnesota in 1966. The U of M has a long history as a global innovator in nearly all types of organ transplants, including heart, lung, kidney, intestine, and bone marrow.

| mninvents.com | designreplace.com |

Organ Transplants

INVENTS

PULSE RATE

OUTPUT

ON

FIRST BATTERY-OPERATED
— EXTERNAL —
PACEMAKER

MEDTRONIC INC.

OFF

1958 Earl Bakken, Medtronic

Inspired by the circuit for an electronic metronome, engineering genius and Medtronic co-founder Earl Bakken created the first battery-powered external pacemaker. This compact device replaced the much larger, cart-bound type, which was also susceptible to power outages.

| mninvents.com | designreplace.com |

BATTERY-OPERATED PACEMAKER
Earl Bakken, Medtronic (1958)

Mad Science Meets Medicine!

In 1958, Earl Bakken created a new type of external artificial pacemaker. Though now considered a Minnesota medical pioneer, Bakken was not a doctor, but rather a humble electrical engineer with a childhood fascination with the famous—and infamous!—fictional character Victor von Frankenstein. He first came to the field of medicine when he was hired to maintain electronic equipment in hospitals. Seeing the potential of these devices eventually led him to found Medtronic (*medical + electronic*—get it?).

The genesis of Bakken's innovative iteration of the pacemaker lay in the necessities of treating babies born prematurely. Previous pacemakers required surgeries that weren't possible on small subjects, and a noninvasive solution was needed. Dr. C. Walton Lillehei approached Bakken about a battery-operated device when a power outage led to the death of one of his patients. Basing his design on a circuit diagram for a metronome, Bakken made medical history.

Today, Medtronic is the world's largest stand-alone medical technology company, and it maintains a museum in Minneapolis dedicated to the history of electronic medicine. The Bakken Museum includes a noteworthy exhibit that re-creates scenes from Mary Shelley's *Frankenstein*, the story that electrified the young Earl Bakken and set the stage for his shockingly useful innovations.

Zap!

SCOTCH #100 AUDIOTAPE
3M (1946)

Fast-Forward into the Future of Audio!

The idea of recording sound on a spool of long, thin something-or-other goes all the way back to the 1890s. First it was wire, and then came steel tape, and then tape made of coated paper. In the 1940s, a Cleveland firm called the Brush Development Company was in the forefront of developing audio recorders, but they needed help perfecting the sound medium. They approached the researchers at Minnesota Mining and Manufacturing Co. in 1944, looking for some bright ideas about magnetic tape.

3M got on board, and the company's labs soon produced the paper-backed Scotch Magnetic Tape #100, which would evolve into the acetate-backed, high-quality #111 and #112. And thus was born a major American industry.

The force behind the popularization of high-fidelity tape recording wasn't all techies and salesmen, though. A huge leg-up came from Bing Crosby, American singer and best-selling recording artist of the 20th century. The overworked Crosby simply didn't want to sing so many live radio shows, and he realized that audiotape would let him broadcast pre-recorded songs that sounded just as good as the live versions. His active interest would help drive the technology's development, and thanks to the new thin and durable tape, those spinning spools would bring about an audio revolution.

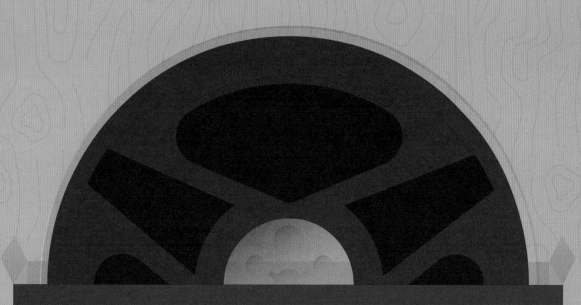

Scotch

CONSUMER MAGNETIC AUDIOTAPE

#100

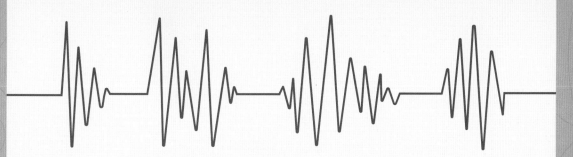

M INVENTS

1946 **Scotch #100 Magnetic Audio Tape, 3M** | mninvents.com | designreplace.com |

Scotch #100 Magnetic Tape was the first successfully mass-produced, consumer-grade magnetic audiotape. It was made of paper tape coated with black oxide. Within a couple of years, the paper backing would be replaced by more flexible and durable acetate.

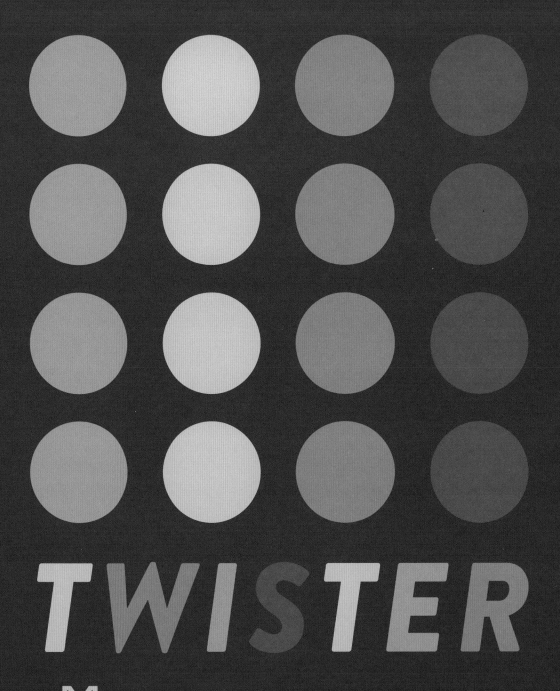

TWISTER

MN INVENTS™

1966 **Reyn Guyer, C. Foley & N. Rabens**
The collaborators developed the human
pretzel party game in the mid-1960s. Milton Bradley bought it
and named it Twister. Its real break came in 1966 when
Johnny Carson and Eva Gabor played it on *The Tonight Show*.

| **mninvents.com** | **designreplace.com** |

TWISTER
Reyn Guyer, Neil Rabens & Charles Foley (1966)

The Game that Made Shy Minnesotans Touch Each Other!

Minnesota Master of Amusements, Reyn Guyer, invented Twister, along with colleagues Neil Rabens and Charles F. Foley. He produced his prototype, which he called Pretzel, while working as a young designer at his father's design company. With its colorful, carpet-size play mat and spinning dial, Twister wasn't a complicated game, but it had an ingenious twist: It used the players themselves as game pieces! Hence its marketing slogan, "The game that ties you up in knots!"

The source of Twister's popularity was the fun to be had tangling people up, limb over undignified limb and torso over torso, on the multicolored mat. At first, though, that scenario struck some folks as a little too racy, and the game was in danger of being pulled from the market by manufacturer Milton Bradley's distributors. But then Johnny Carson and Eva Gabor played a round of Twister on an episode of *The Tonight Show*, and huge demand materialized overnight. Reyn Guyer, meantime, didn't rest on his laurels, going on to invent Nerf and many other famous toys.

FIRST MODERN SKYWAY
First National Bank Building, St. Paul (1931)

The Big Red One!

There's a skyway in downtown St. Paul that plugs into the top floor of the Merchants Bank Building, a 16-story structure that opened in 1916. At the other end of it is the 17th floor of the iconic First National Bank Building. Which means that this first modern skyway connects the building that was once the city's tallest with the one it would lose that title to (and that would hold on to it for the next 55 years).

The First National Bank Building was designed by Chicago's Graham, Anderson, Probst & White, America's largest architectural firm at the time. They were also responsible for many Chicago landmarks, including the Wrigley Building, the Merchandise Mart, the Field Museum of Natural History, Shedd Aquarium, and the Civic Opera House.

In spite of a scarcity of building materials caused by the construction of New York's Empire State Building, First National Bank's builders completed the structure in 1931. Today, crowned by its classic red neon "1st," it is a shining staple of our state capital's spectacular skyline.

M INVENTS

1968 Jeno Paulucci, Aurora, MN
The popular snack came about in an attempt to find alternative uses for egg roll wrappers. Pillsbury later bought Jeno's Pizza Rolls for $140 million. | mninvents.com | designreplace.com |

PIZZA ROLLS
Jeno Paulucci, Aurora, MN (1968)

Bite-Size Pockets of Burning-Hot Brilliance!

In the mid-1970s, pizza pioneer Jeno F. Paulucci unleashed a microwaveable marvel on an unsuspecting North. Modeled on the Chinese egg roll, the instantly popular, piping-hot pizza roll first saw the light of day in Duluth, Minnesota.

Paulucci was a monumental figure and a microwave magnate. A self-described "serial entrepreneur," he was an inventor, an investor, and a proud publisher of a magazine dedicated to Italian-American businessmen. He was also pro-union and a proponent of a higher minimum wage for his workers, and when, despite his ardent advocacy of Minnesota business, he moved pizza production from Duluth to Cleveland, Ohio, he vowed to return all 7,600 lost jobs to the region.

In 1985, Paulucci sold the pizza roll to Totino's, a move he would regret for the rest of career. "I should've kept the pizza roll," he lamented, saying it was "something that would live forever." Jeno himself lived until 2014, leaving behind a $100 million estate and a legacy of scorched mouths and satisfied snackers!

POP-UP TOASTER
Charles Strite, Stillwater, MN (1919)

Launching Bread to New Heights!

Charles Strite had a problem: burnt toast. Toasting bread required a certain amount of attention and diligence in the early 20th century, and the toast in Strite's workplace cafeteria in Stillwater, Minnesota, just wasn't getting them. Fed up with the situation, the master mechanic came up with an ingenious solution, and in 1919 he filed a patent for a toaster that incorporated springs and a timer. Imagine: A gadget that, at the exact moment of golden-brown perfection, would shut off the heat and, with a satisfying *boing!*, present your toast to you like a beribboned birthday present. Could it get any better than this?!

Strite formed the Waters-Genter Company to manufacture his product, which he thought would sell primarily to restaurants. But further improvements and a dynamic new name, the Toastmaster (which became the name of the company too), combined with the arrival of pre-sliced bread in the 1930s, brought a surge in demand for home use. Now, virtually no home is without a toaster—evidence of Charles Strite's bright idea seems to pop up all over the place!

MN INVENTS™ 1ST POP-UP TOASTER

1919 Charles Strite, Stillwater, MN
Charles Strite got tired of eating burnt toast in his workplace cafeteria in Stillwater. To remedy the problem, he designed a spring-loaded toaster with a built-in timer.

| mninvents.com | designreplace.com |

water skis!

Water in Minnesota is generally in the form of ice for half the year.

Minnesota is one of the most landlocked spots in North America.

WATER SKIS
Ralph Samuelson, Lake City, MN (1922)

"If you can ski on snow, then you can ski on water." —Ralph Samuelson

The water in Minnesota's 10,000 lakes is frozen solid for half the year. In other words, here, 2,000 miles from the nearest ocean, water in wintertime has always been something you travel on top of. And an intrepid northern sportsmen like Ralph Samuelson wasn't about to let a little thing like summer change that.

Samuelson was the first person to attempt to ride the waves pulled by a boat, with a pair of barrel staves lashed to his feet. It didn't work. He tried snow skis next, but again to no avail. A little more R&D eventually produced a pair of skis 8 feet long by 9 inches wide, with the front tips bent up and leather straps for securing his feet. With his brother at the helm, Samuelson rode those down Lake Pepin, reaching a speed of 20 miles per hour.

Soon he began showing off his new sport across the United States, while finding ways to up the ante. On July 8, 1925, after smearing lard on a half-sunken diving platform, he jumped a height of 60 feet off its raised end, making him the first-ever water ski jumper. That same year, he hooked himself up behind a 200-horsepower World War I flying boat and hit 80 miles per hour. All this public relations work succeeded brilliantly: Water skiing became an instant sensation, guaranteeing Ralph Samuelson a big, foamy, unforgettable wake in the history of aquatic recreation.

A NOTE FROM THE AUTHORS

Like all great stories, the rivers of legend surrounding Minnesota inventions are deep and wide. Some of these mighty tributaries have, understandably, rolled into various versions of the storyline. As with all legends, it is important to recognize that all perspectives surrounding these inventions, inventors, and stories are all valid and important. It is equally important to recognize that some of these accountings may differ from the Wikipedia-approved version of historical events. We hope these stories inspire you to break open your own understanding of invention, both in Minnesota and beyond.

Each one of these great stories could easily fill a thousand pages on its own. We hope you will dig deeper into each story, and they will help you write your own history of Minnesota Invention.

ABOUT REPLACE

Replace is an international award-winning team of artists + writers that specialize in brand design. Founded in 1996, our Minneapolis firm approaches all projects believing that you are in business to Improve + Replace the status quo. Clients like you make us great. Our work is in the Cooper Hewitt, Smithsonian Design Museum, the Minnesota Historical Society, the American Institute of Graphic Arts, the Walker Art Center, and most likely somewhere in your home.

REPLACE